film songs of the 90s

Production: Stephen Clark and Sadie Cook

Design and Typesetting by Xheight Limited

Published 1995

© **International Music Publications Limited**
Southend Road, Woodford Green, Essex IG8 8HN, England

BOHEMIAN RHAPSODY

Words and Music by
FREDDIE MERCURY

4

Didn't mean to make you cry, If I'm not back again this time to-
I don't want to die, I some-times wish I'd nev-er been born at

mor-row, car-ry on, car-ry on as if noth-ing real-ly mat-ters.

Instrumental Solo

all.

Instrumental Solo

L'istesso tempo

I see a lit-tle sil-hou-et-to of a man, Scar-a-

mouche, Scar-a-mouche, will you do the Fan-dan-go. Thun-der-bolt and light-ning, ver-y, ver-y fright-'ning

Chorus:

6

9

CAN'T HELP FALLING IN LOVE

Words and Music by GEORGE WEISS,
HUGH PERETTI and LUIDI CREATORE

END OF THE ROAD

Words and Music by KENNY EDMONDS,
ANTONIO REID and DARYL SIMMONS

Come to the end of the__ road,__ still I can't let___ you

go.__ It's un-nat-ur-al. You be-long to me, I be-long to you.__

-long to me, I be-long to you. Al-though we've -long to me, I be-long to you.__

Verse 2:
Girl, I know you really love me, you just don't realize.
You've never been there before, it's only your first time.
Maybe I'll forgive you, mmm. . . maybe you'll try.
We should be happy together, forever, you and I.

Bridge 2:
Could you love me again like you loved me before?
This time, I want you to love me much more.
This time, instead just come back to my bed.
And baby, just don't let me down.

Verse 3, spoken:
Girl I'm here for you.
All those times at night when you just hurt me,
And just ran out with that other fellow,
Baby, I knew about it.
I just didn't care.
You just don't understand how much I love you, do you?
I'm here for you.
I'm not out to go out there and cheat all night just like you did, baby.
But that's alright, huh, I love you anyway.
And I'm still gonna be here for you 'til my dyin' day, baby.
Right now, I'm just in so much pain, baby,
'Cause you just won't come back to me, will you?
Just come back to me.

Bridge 3, spoken:
Yes, baby, my heart is lonely.
My heart hurts, baby, yes, I feel pain too.
Baby please . . .

(EVERYTHING I DO) I DO IT FOR YOU

Words and Music by BRYAN ADAMS,
R J LANGE and M KAMEN

more___ love. There's no - where___ un - less you're___ there, all the

time,_____ all the way,___ yeah.___

dim. *mf*

(instrumental solo . . .

1. | 2.

Oh, you can't tell me it's not worth try - in'

. . . end solo)

I WILL ALWAYS LOVE YOU

Words and Music by
DOLLY PARTON

Verse 3: Instrumental solo

Verse 4:
I hope life treats you kind
And I hope you have all you've dreamed of.
And I wish to you, joy and happiness.
But above all this, I wish you love.
(To Chorus:)

I'M GONNA BE (500 MILES)

Words and Music by
CHARLES REID and CRAIG REID

30

D.%.%. al Coda 2

CODA 2

com-ing home _____ wi' you. But da. And I would walk five hun-dred miles and I_ _ would walk five hun-dred more just to be the man who walked a thou-sand miles to fall down at your door. _____

IN ALL THE RIGHT PLACES

Words by LISA STANSFIELD,
IAN DEVANEY and ANDY MORRIS
Music by JOHN BARRY

Moderate rock ♩ = 92

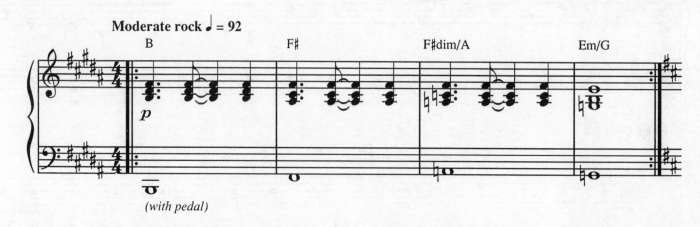

(with pedal)

Verse:

If you take me straight to heav - en, I could nev - er fall.___

'Cause lov-ing you is what I'm made_ for, I'd glad-ly give my all - in - all.___

It does-n't mat - ter where___ I am,___ as long as I'm with you.___

in a crowd-ed room,___ when you wrap your arms a-round_ me,

you al-ways send me to the moon._ When we kiss our sug-ar kiss - es

and the mu - sic starts to play,_ we've got love, we've got each oth - er

and we're go - in' all the way._ In all___ the right plac-es,

cresc.

Chorus:

mf

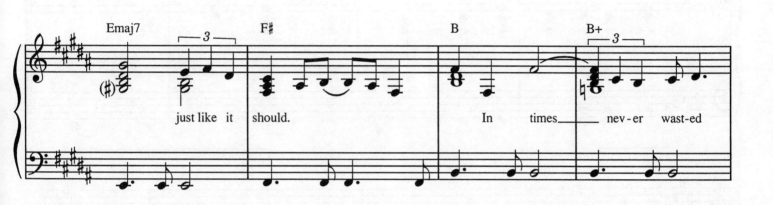

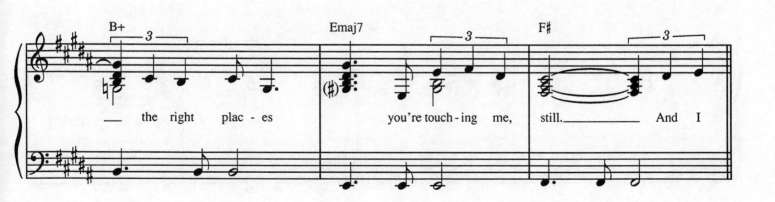

LOVE IS IN THE AIR

Words and Music by
HARRY VANDA and GEORGE YOUNG

IT MUST HAVE BEEN LOVE

Words and Music by
PER GESSLE

A KISS TO BUILD A DREAM ON

Words and Music by BERT KALMAR,
HARRY RUBY and OSCAR HAMMERSTEIN II

Give me a kiss to build a dream on and my im-ag-i-
Give me a kiss be-fore you leave me and my im-ag-i-
Give me your lips for just a mo-ment and my im-ag-i-

na-tion will thrive up-on that kiss.
na-tion will feed my hun-gry heart.
na-tion will make that mo-ment live.

Sweet-heart, I ask no more than
Leave me one thing be-fore we
Give me what you a-lone can

this, a kiss to build a dream on.____
part, a kiss to build a
give, a kiss to build a

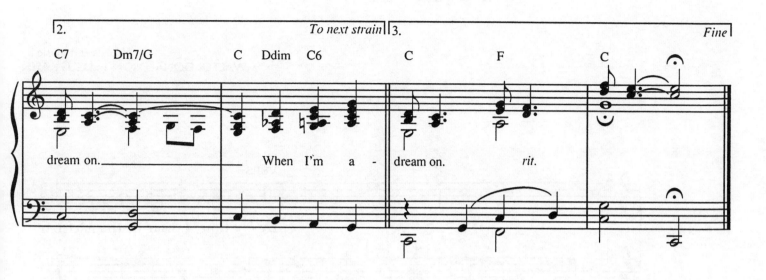

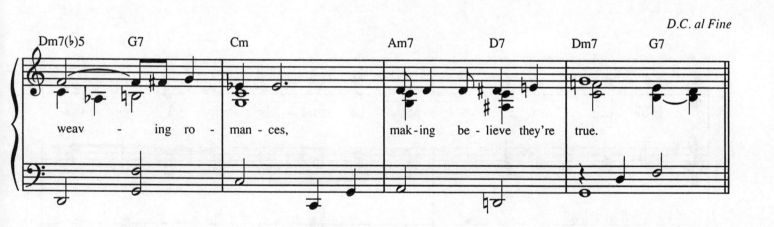

MAKIN' WHOOPEE!

Words and Music by
WALTER DONALDSON and GUS KAHN

MUSTANG SALLY

Words and Music by
BONNY RICE

Mus-tang Sal-

Verse:

ly,   guess you bet-ter   slow that Mus-tang   down.

Mus-tang

Sal-ly, now ba - by,   guess you bet-ter   slow that Mus-tang   down.

You been

run-nin' all__ o - ver town,__ ooh,__ I guess you got-ta put your flat feet

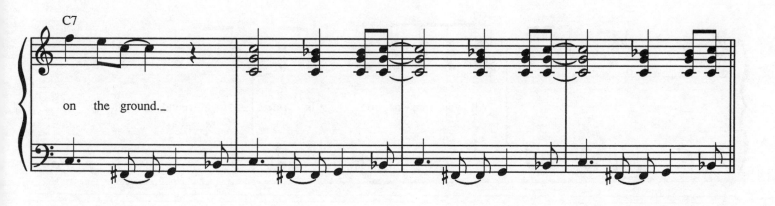

on the ground.__

Chorus:

All you wan-na do is ride__ a-round, Sal-ly. (Ride, Sal-ly,__ ride.__)

All you wan-na do is ride___ a-round, Sal-ly. (Ride, Sal-ly___ ride.___)

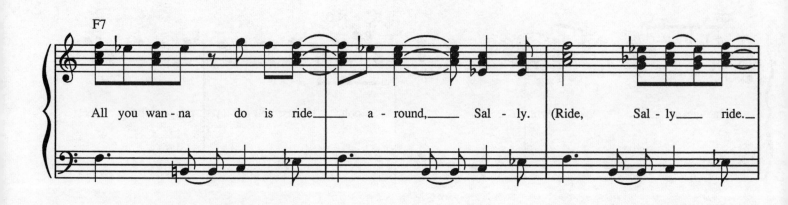

All you wan - na do is ride___ a - round,___ Sal - ly. (Ride, Sal - ly___ ride.___

___) All you wan-na do is ride___ a - round, Sal - ly.

(Ride, Sal - ly,___ ride.___) One of these ear - ly morn-

Verse 2:
I bought you a brand new Mustang,
It was a nineteen sixty five.
Now you come around, signifying a woman.
Girl, you won't, you won't let me ride.
Mustang Sally, now baby,
Guess you better slow that Mustang down.
You been runnin' all over town.
Oh, guess you gotta put your flat feet on the ground.
(To Chorus:)

MY GIRL

Words and Music by
WILLIAM ROBINSON and RONALD WHITE

57

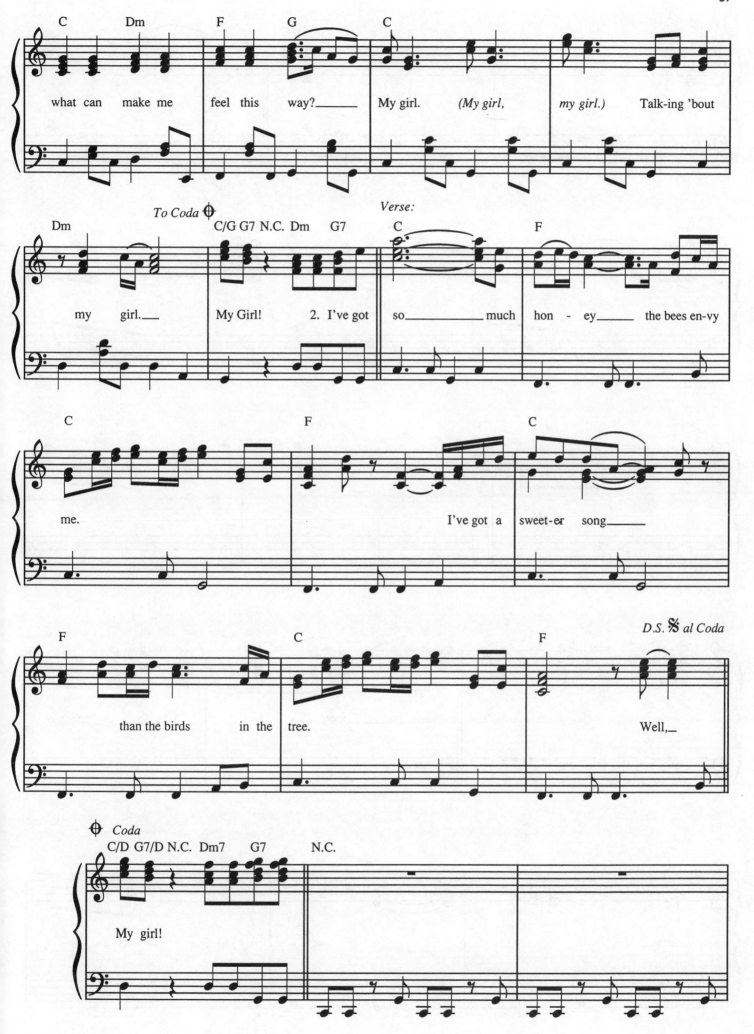

MY GUY

Words and Music by
WILLIAM ROBINSON

61

SIGH NO MORE LADIES

Words by WILLIAM SHAKESPEARE
Music by PATRICK DOYLE

ONE LOVE

Words and Music by
TONY KINSEY

One love,___ I knew but one love,___ my
Mem - 'ries,___ so ma - ny mem - 'ries,___ a

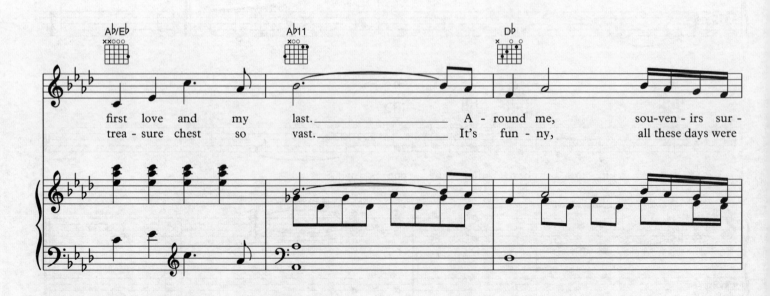

first love and my last._____ A - round me, sou - ven - irs sur -
trea - sure chest so vast._____ It's fun - ny, all these days were

- round me,   all the sou-ven - irs   of true love passed.
sun - ny,   now they're sou-ven - irs   of true love

passed.   A   ring,_____ a pho-to - graph or two,_____ some flowers_____ pressed in a
him_____ I wish I could re-turn,_____ for that_____ I'd give my

book,   locks of hair, all en-twined mean-ing   I love you.
life,   we were young, now it's clear that we   did - n't learn.

Tok - ens of the day, when I heard you say, lov-ing you has al-ways been my
We'd found per-fect love, true and last - ing love, not for just a day but for e -

des - ti - ny. Now I see clear - ly,___ I see so clear - ly,_____ my
- ter - ni - ty.

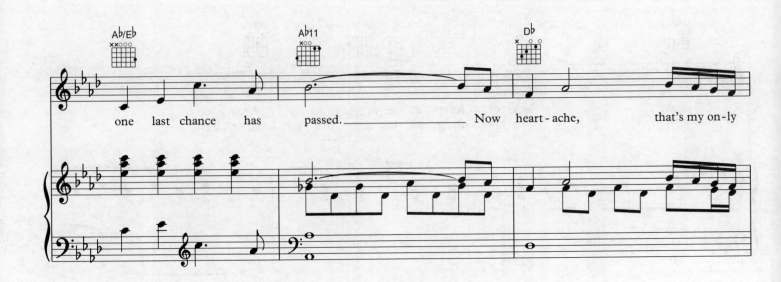

one last chance has passed._____ Now heart - ache, that's my on-ly

keep - sake, just a sou-ven - ir of true love passed. To

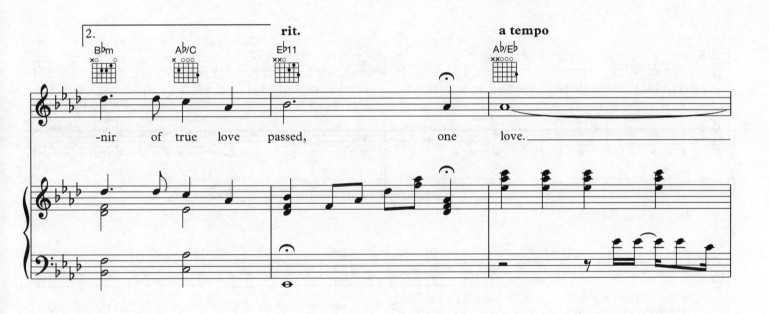

-nir of true love passed, one love.

THE SHOOP SHOOP SONG
(IT'S IN HIS KISS)

Words and Music by
RUDY CLARK

SHOW ME HEAVEN

Words and Music by JAY RIFKIN,
ERIC RACKIN and MARIA McKEE

show me hea - ven, co - ver me, leave me breath - less,

oh, show me hea - ven please.

If you know what it's like to dream a dream,

ba - by hold me tight and let this be, oh,

D.S.

THEME FROM 'DISCLOSURE'

By ENNIO MORRICONE

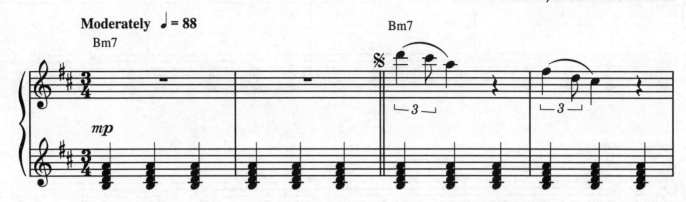

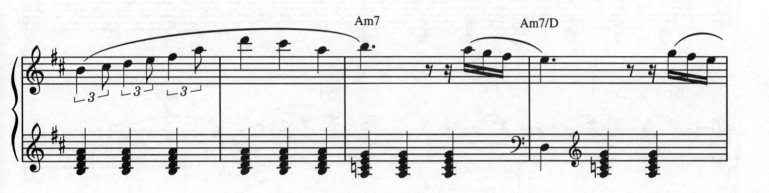

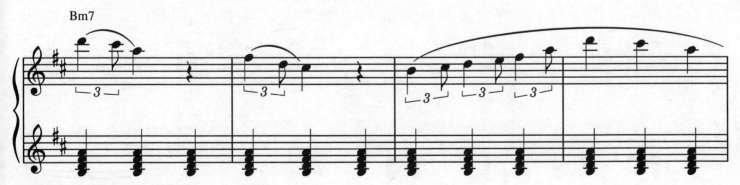

SMILE

Words by JOHN TURNER and GEOFFREY PARSONS
Music by CHARLES CHAPLIN

STAR DUST
(ETOILE D'AMOUR)

Words by MITCHELL PARISH
French translation by YVETTE BARUCH
Music by HOAGY CARMICHAEL

TAKE ME TO THE RIVER

Words and Music by AL GREEN
and MABON LEWIS HODGES

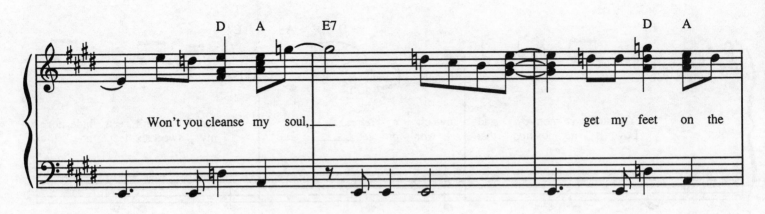

Won't you cleanse my soul, ____ get my feet on the

ground.

To Coda | 1. | 2. *To Next Strain* | 3. *D.S.S. al Coda*

Bridge:

Hold ___ me, love ___ me, squeeze ___ me, _____

tease ___ me till I die, ___ till I die. ___

WICKED GAME

Words and Music by
CHRIS ISAAK

YOU'RE MY BEST FRIEND

Words and Music by
JOHN DEACON

WHEN I FALL IN LOVE

Words by EDWARD HEYMAN
Music by VICTOR YOUNG

See page 100 for Introduction and Verse

REFRAIN

When I fall in love it will be for-ev-er, Or I'll nev-er fall in

love._____ In a rest-less world like this is, love is end-ed be-fore it's be-

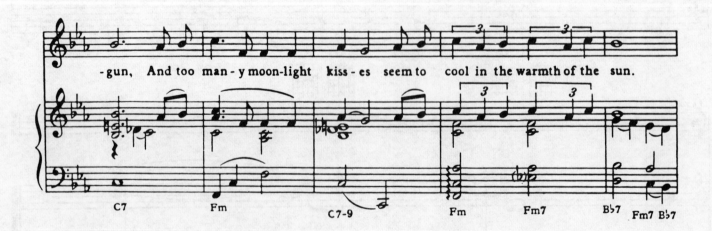

-gun, And too man-y moon-light kiss-es seem to cool in the warmth of the sun.

INTRODUCTION AND VERSE

Printed by
Halstan & Co. Ltd., Amersham, Bucks., England